Published by
Storysack Ltd.
Resource House, Kay Street,
Bury BL9 6BU

In association with
European Space Agency

ISBN 978-1-904949-03-9

Text © Stuart and Nicola Clark 2005
Based on an original idea by Neil Griffiths
Photographs © ESA/NASA 2005
Illustrations © Janette Louden 2005
First published in the UK 2005
Reprinted with audio CD 2011

Design by
David Rose

Illustrated by
Janette Louden and Mark Slader

Education Consultant
ESA Education, Anne Brumfitt

Printed in China

LITTLE MOON

by **Stuart** and **Nicola Clark**

Based on an original idea by Neil Griffiths

published in association with

◗esa

Little Moon was born a long time ago,
far away in space. It was so cold where
he was born that Little Moon shivered.
"I need to warm up," he thought and
he set off to find somewhere cosier.

He looked around and saw a
bright star in the distance. It
was yellow and looked warm.
 "That's where I'll go!"
said Little Moon and off he set.

Soon, he saw two worlds. Both were covered in ice.
"I'm the planet Pluto," said one.
"And I'm his moon," said the other.
Little Moon watched as they twirled around each
other as if they were dancing. There was
nowhere for him to fit in, so he moved
on towards the yellow star.

Then Little Moon found another planet.
It was big and blue.
  "Hello, who are you?" asked Little Moon shyly.
"May I live here?"
The planet turned a cold eye on him and said,
  "I'm Neptune and I already have six moons. Why
would I want any more? Shoo!"
Little Moon quickly moved on towards the yellow star.

The next planet was lying on its side, spinning over and over instead of round and round.

"I'm Uranus and I've fallen over. Can you help me up?" asked the planet.

"I don't think so, I'm not strong enough," said Little Moon. "And you're making me feel dizzy."

"Well there's no point in you staying then," Uranus said grumpily and started to sulk.

Little Moon decided to move on towards the yellow star.

Still feeling a little dizzy, Little Moon suddenly saw a very large planet. It was yellow and looked as if it was wearing a skirt.

"That's not a skirt!" said the planet. "I'm Saturn and these are my rings." Little Moon looked closer and saw that the rings were made of pebbles and stones. They were all pretty colours and shone in the sunlight.

Saturn had a big family of small moons.
"Come and play," called the moons as they chased each
other around the planet. "We run around all day and all night."
Little Moon joined in, but soon ran out of breath.
"I can't keep up!" he said.

"That's a shame, because we never
stop," said the moons, still running.
So little Moon waved goodbye and
moved on towards the yellow star.

In the distance, Little Moon spied a giant planet ahead of him. As he came closer, he could see it was an exciting place. It was covered in swirling clouds and sometimes flashed with lightning. A great red spot spun round and round like a giant hurricane.

"I'm Jupiter, King of the planets," boomed the planet.

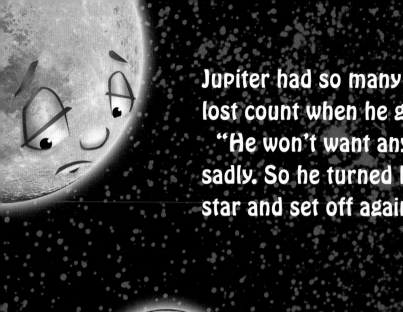

Jupiter had so many moons, that Little Moon
lost count when he got to sixty!
"He won't want any more," he thought
sadly. So he turned his back on the yellow
star and set off again back into deep space.

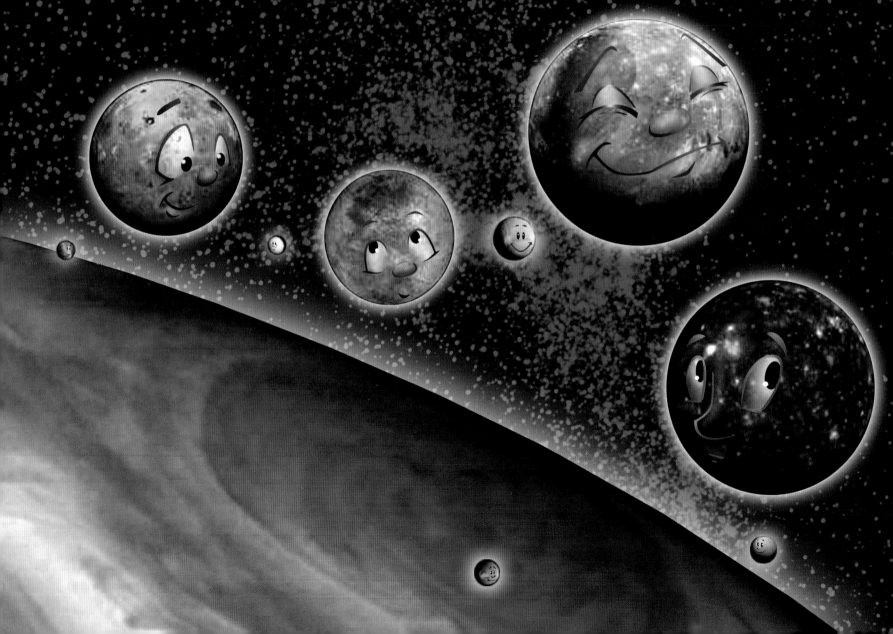

Little Moon found himself in a cloud of many colours. It was a quiet and calm place, with no one else around. Soon, Little Moon felt lonely and began searching for someone to talk to.

As Little Moon searched deeper into the cloud, he saw stars bursting into life from giant pockets of swirling mist.
"Wow!" said Little Moon, "This must be a star nursery."
He shouted "Hello" to them, but the baby stars could not talk. They just chuckled and squealed.
Little Moon smiled and moved on.

Back in deep space, Little Moon suddenly felt himself being pulled along. He went faster and faster until he was whizzing round in a big circle. It was quite fun at first, but then he became dizzy. He tried to stop himself moving but couldn't. He started to feel frightened.

"What's happening to me?"
he shouted.

A strange voice laughed with an evil cackle.
"I'm a black hole and you look very tasty."
"What do you mean?" cried Little Moon.
"I'm going to eat you," said the black
hole. "I'm always hungry."

Terrified, Little Moon summoned
all his strength and jumped away
from the black hole at the last
minute before he was swallowed.
He rushed away as fast as he
could, relieved to have escaped.

Little Moon began to cry.
"What's the matter?"
asked a kind voice.
Little Moon looked up and
saw something coming
towards him with an
enormous, bright tail.

"I'm lost and have nowhere to live and I
was nearly eaten by a black hole," he sobbed.
"Follow my tail," said the comet. "I know
where to take you."

Little Moon followed the comet and soon realised
they were heading back towards the yellow star.
"But I've been there already and none of the
planets I met liked me," said Little Moon sadly.

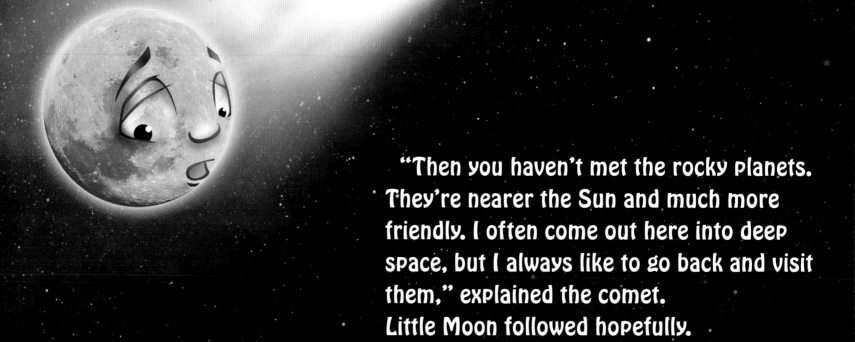

"Then you haven't met the rocky planets.
They're nearer the Sun and much more
friendly. I often come out here into deep
space, but I always like to go back and visit
them," explained the comet.
Little Moon followed hopefully.

They travelled together towards the Sun, avoiding the larger planets. They reached a crowd of asteroids.

"These are my cousins," said the comet, waving to the lumps of rock.

"But they don't look like you," said a puzzled Little Moon.

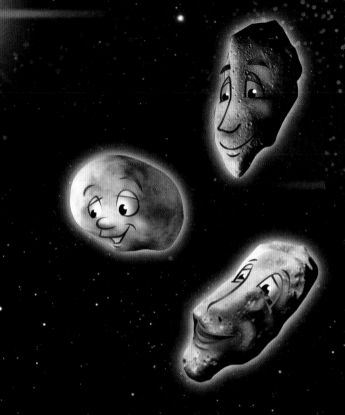

"I'm not just a tail!" said the comet. "I have a little body made of ice and rocks too. Asteroids don't have ice or a tail, but they are rocks and they go around the Sun." Together they dodged in and out of the asteroids and moved towards the Sun.

Soon, they came to a red planet.
  "This is Mars and her two tiny moons,"
said the comet. "I can't stop, but why
don't you stay for a chat?"
Mars and her moons did seem friendly,
so Little Moon thought it was a good idea.
Little Moon watched the comet race on,
waving its enormous tail across space.

Little Moon saw that Mars was very old.

   "I used to be beautiful," she said. "I had oceans, seas and rivers.
Now I'm just rocks and rubble. But I'm still happy. You see, not
every rocky planet has moons and I have two."

   "Where are the planets without moons?" asked Little Moon.

   "Perhaps I can make my home with one of those?"

   "Keep going towards the Sun and you'll find three of them, dear,"
said Mars. So Little Moon smiled back at her and hurried off to find them.

Little Moon whizzed off so quickly that he shot straight past the three planets and ended up at the Sun. It was far too bright and much too hot, but he stayed long enough to watch its surface boiling. Suddenly, a giant explosion burst out from the Sun, throwing a huge ball of gas towards him. Little Moon turned around and ran.

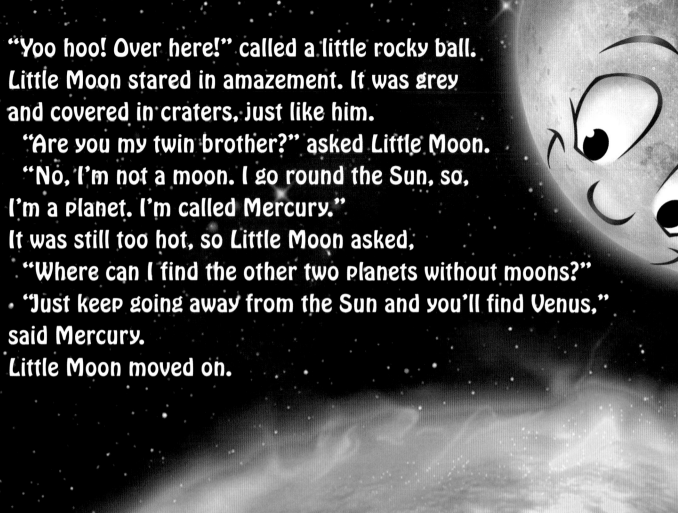

"Yoo hoo! Over here!" called a little rocky ball.
Little Moon stared in amazement. It was grey
and covered in craters, just like him.
   "Are you my twin brother?" asked Little Moon.
   "No, I'm not a moon. I go round the Sun, so,
I'm a planet. I'm called Mercury."
It was still too hot, so Little Moon asked,
   "Where can I find the other two planets without moons?"
   "Just keep going away from the Sun and you'll find Venus,"
said Mercury.
Little Moon moved on.

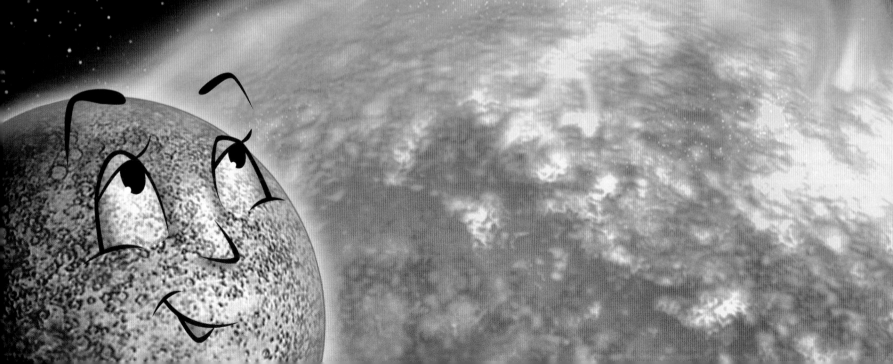

Venus was fast asleep,
wrapped up in
blankets of cloud.
 "Hello," called
Little Moon.
Venus did not answer.

"Wake up!"

shouted Little Moon.

Venus peeped out and yawned.
 "Sorry, I can't talk now. I need
my beauty sleep." With that, she
went straight back to sleep.
 "It won't be much fun living here
if she sleeps all the time," thought
Little Moon, so he moved on.

"Only one more chance. Will I ever find a home?"
Little Moon wondered.
Then suddenly, he saw the most beautiful planet
ever! It had big, blue oceans with white clouds and
there were green and brown patches of land.
  "Hello, my name's Earth. Are you a moon?"
the planet asked.
Little Moon nodded.
        "I've always wanted a moon for a friend,"
          said Earth, eagerly. "Why don't you stay
            and be my moon?"
              "Can I?" shouted Little Moon,
              excitedly.
                "Yes. Would you like to
                 dance to celebrate?"
                 Earth grinned at
                 Little Moon.

So Little Moon
stayed and danced
with the Earth.

"I'm not lost any more. I've found
a lovely home." Little Moon smiled.
In fact, Little Moon didn't stop
smiling and even now, if you look up
at the Moon, sometimes you can see
his happy face, smiling down at you.

Go on, take a
look tonight!